There's no such thing as. Work-life Balance. The are Work-life Choice's.

Notebook

Made in the USA
Middletown, DE
16 February 2023

25004240R00057